Humpty Dumpty

& other rhymes

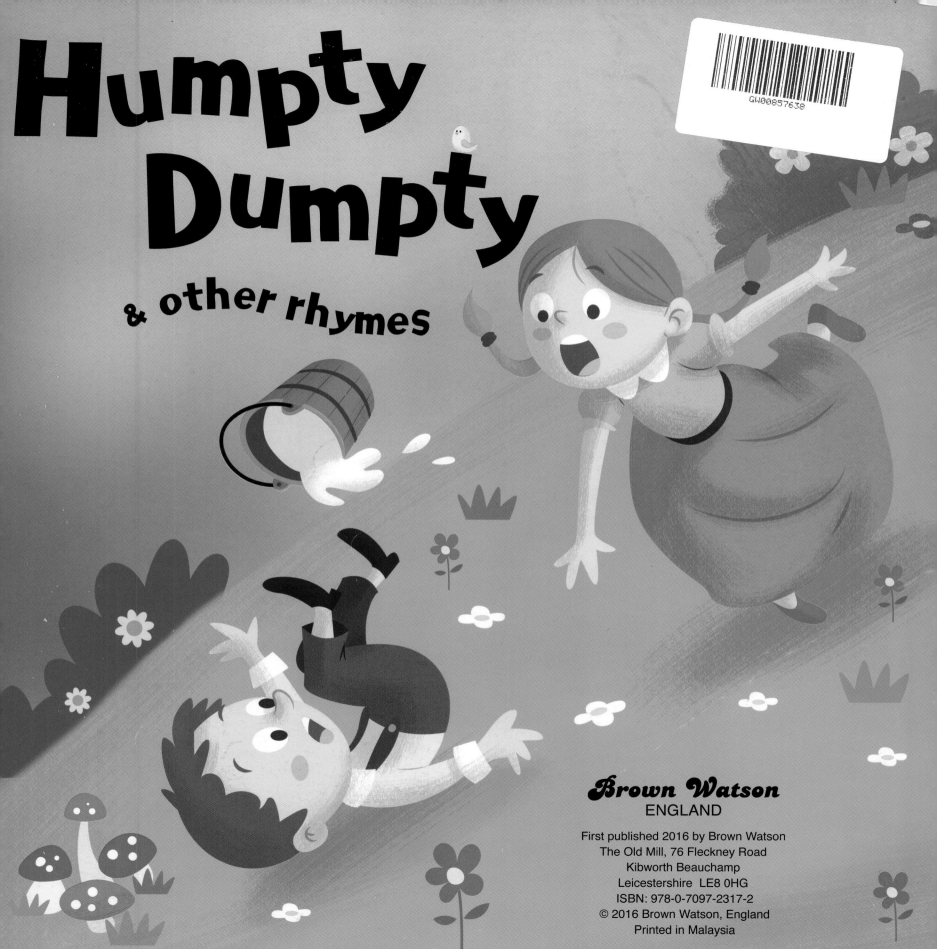

Brown Watson
ENGLAND

First published 2016 by Brown Watson
The Old Mill, 76 Fleckney Road
Kibworth Beauchamp
Leicestershire LE8 0HG
ISBN: 978-0-7097-2317-2
© 2016 Brown Watson, England
Printed in Malaysia

Humpty Dumpty

Humpty Dumpty sat on a wall,
Humpty Dumpty had a great fall.
All the king's horses and
all the king's men,
Couldn't put Humpty
together again.

I'm a Little Teapot

I'm a little teapot,
Short and stout.
Here's my handle,
Here's my spout.
When I see the teacups,
Hear me shout:
'Tip me over and pour me out!'

Wee Willie Winkie

Wee Willie Winkie runs through the town,
Upstairs and downstairs in his nightgown,
Tapping at the window and crying
through the lock,
Are all the children in their beds,
it's past eight o'clock?

Mary had a Little Lamb

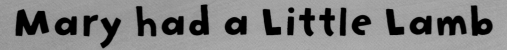

Mary had a little lamb,
Its fleece was white as snow;
And everywhere that Mary went
The lamb was sure to go.

He followed her to school one day
Which was against the rule;
It made the children laugh and play,
To see a lamb at school.

Hey Diddle Diddle

Hey diddle diddle, the cat and the fiddle,
The cow jumped over the moon.
The little dog laughed to see such fun
And the dish ran away with the spoon!

Little Miss Muffet

Little Miss Muffet
Sat on a tuffet,
Eating her curds and whey;
Along came a spider,
Who sat down beside her,
And frightened Miss Muffet away.

The Queen of Hearts

The Queen of Hearts
She made some tarts,
All on a summer's day;
The Knave of Hearts
He stole those tarts,
And took them clean away.
The King of Hearts
Called for the tarts,
And beat the knave full sore;
The Knave of Hearts
Brought back the tarts,
And vowed he'd steal no more.

Little Bo-Peep

Little Bo-Peep has lost her sheep,
And doesn't know where to find them;
Leave them alone, and they'll come home,
Wagging their tails behind them.

There Was an Old Woman

There was an old woman who lived in a shoe.
She had so many children, she didn't know what to do;
She gave them some broth without any bread;
She whipped them all soundly and sent them to bed.

Little Jack Horner

Little Jack Horner
Sat in a corner,
Eating his Christmas pie:
He put in his thumb,
And pulled out a plum,
And said,
'What a good boy am I!'

Mary, Mary

Mary, Mary, quite contrary,
How does your garden grow?
With silver bells, and cockle shells,
And pretty maids all in a row.

Old King Cole

Old King Cole
Was a merry old soul,
And a merry old soul was he;
He called for his pipe,
And he called for his bowl,
And he called for his fiddlers three.
Every fiddler he had a fiddle,
And a very fine fiddle had he.
Oh there's none so rare, as can compare
With King Cole and his fiddlers three.

Georgie Porgie

Georgie Porgie, pudding and pie,
Kissed the girls and made them cry.
When the boys came out to play,
Georgie Porgie ran away.

See-Saw Margery Daw

See-saw Margery Daw,
Johnny shall have a new master,
He shall have but a penny a day,
Because he can't work any faster.

Jack and Jill

Jack and Jill went up the hill
To fetch a pail of water.
Jack fell down and broke his crown,
And Jill came tumbling after.

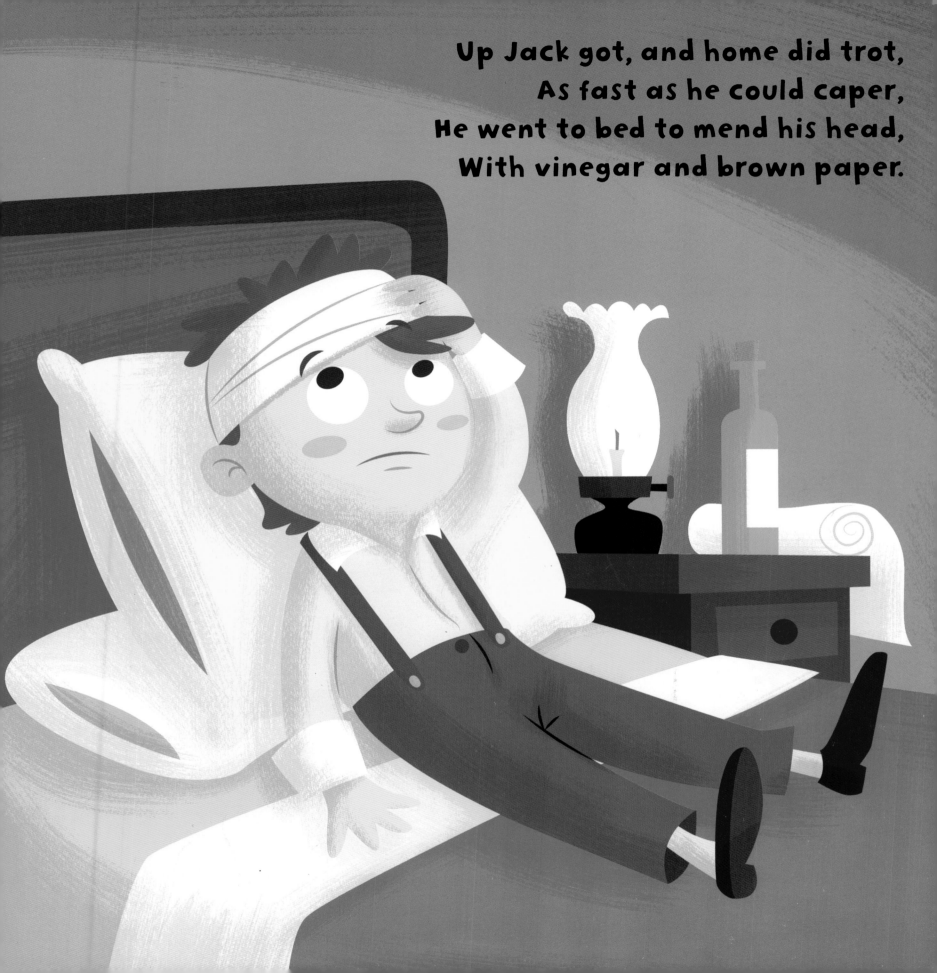

Up Jack got, and home did trot,
As fast as he could caper,
He went to bed to mend his head,
With vinegar and brown paper.

Boys and Girls, Come Out to Play

Boys and girls, come out to play,
The moon doth shine as bright as day;
Leave your supper and leave your sleep,
And come with your playfellows into the street.

Come with a whoop, and come with a call,
Come with a good will, or not at all.
Up the ladder and down the wall,
A halfpenny loaf will serve us all;
You find the milk, and I'll find the flour,
And we'll have a pudding in half-an-hour.

Round and Round the Garden

Round and round the garden,
Like a teddy bear.
One step, two step,
Tickle you under there!

Little Tommy Tittlemouse

Little Tommy Tittlemouse
Lived in a little house;
He caught fishes
In other mens' ditches.

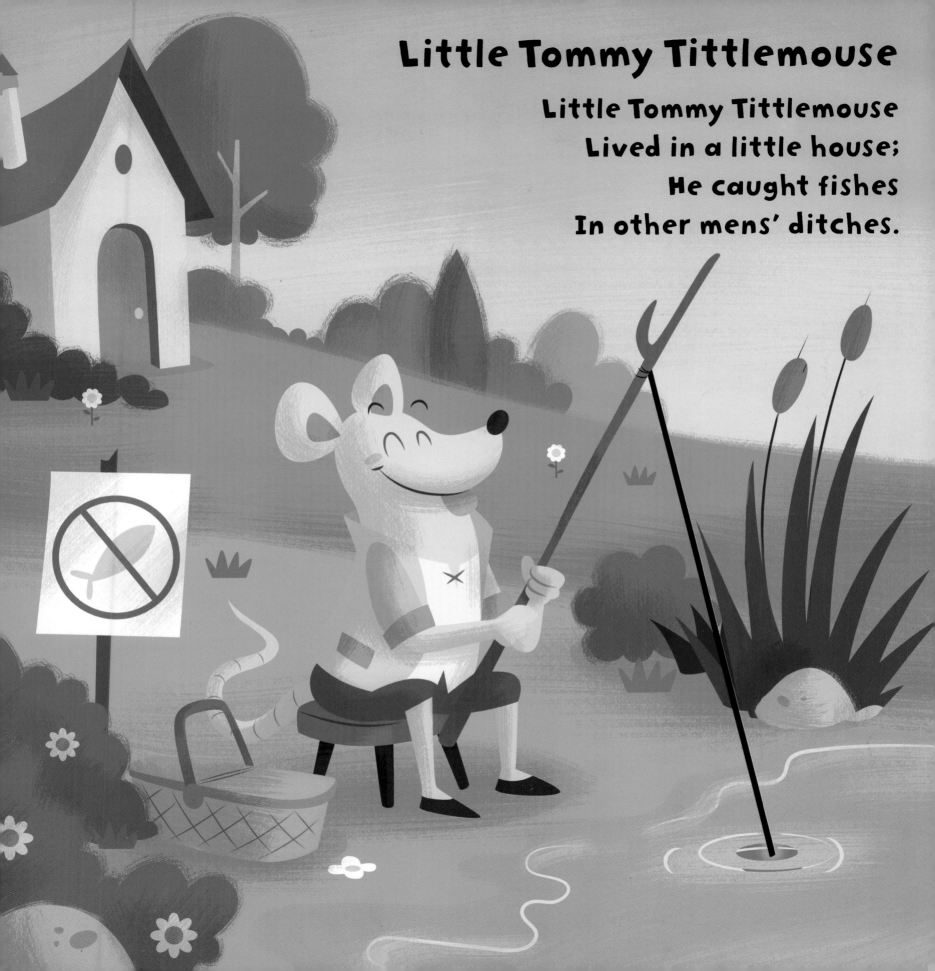

Pat-a-Cake

Pat-a-cake, pat-a-cake, baker's man,
Bake me a cake as fast as you can;
Pat it and shape it and mark it with 'B',
And put it in the oven for baby and me.